Lost Animals

by David Orme

Ransom

D0277869

Trailblazers

Lost Animals
by David Orme
Educational consultant: Helen Bird

Illustrated by Jorge Mongiovi

Published by Ransom Publishing Ltd.
51 Southgate Street, Winchester, Hants. SO23 9EH
www.ransom.co.uk

ISBN   978 184167 807 8
First published in 2009

Lost Animals

Contents

Lost Animals

Get
the
facts

What is extinction?

Sometimes, a species (or type) of animal disappears. We say they become extinct.

Why does this happen?

1 Their habitat changes. This could be because:

- there is a change in the climate.
- their habitat is destroyed by humans.

2 A better-designed animal comes along.

3 They are hunted to extinction.

Usually, we think about people being the hunters. But a new, powerful predator might wipe out a prey species. The predator would have to move on – or die out.

The rain forest is disappearing fast. So are its animals.

4 They are wiped out by alien species or disease.

We don't mean aliens from space! If animals from one country are taken to another one, they can cause big problems for the animals that are already there.

They might:

- eat all the food

- spread a new disease.

Mass extinctions

A  mass extinction is when a whole species, or a large number of species, is wiped out in one go.

The most famous mass extinction was 65 million years ago, when a comet hit the Earth and wiped out the dinosaurs.

Mammals from the past

Ten million years after the dinosaurs were wiped out, **mammals** were the most important animal type.

Some of them were like modern mammals, but some were very different.

How do we know what they looked like?

Even if a **fossil** of only part of the animal is found, scientists can work out what the whole creature was like.

. . . EXTINCT MAMMAL FILES . . .

Name:	Uintatherium	
When it lived:	40 – 45 million years ago	
Type:	Herbivore	
Description:	About the size of a modern rhino.	

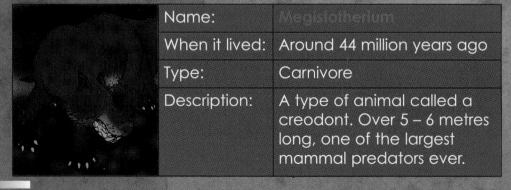

Name:	Megistotherium
When it lived:	Around 44 million years ago
Type:	Carnivore
Description:	A type of animal called a creodont. Over 5 – 6 metres long, one of the largest mammal predators ever.

Name:	Indricotherium
When it lived:	35 million years ago
Type:	Herbivore
Description:	The largest ever land mammal, over 5 metres tall and 8 metres long.

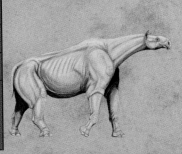

Name:	Aepycamelus
When it lived:	Around 20 million years ago
Type:	Herbivore
Description:	Like a half camel, half giraffe.

Name:	Sabre Tooth Tiger
When it lived:	Became extinct 11,500 years ago
Type:	Carnivore
Description:	About the size of a modern jaguar. Six-inch long, sword-like teeth.

Name:	Woolly Mammoth
When it lived:	Died out 4,500 years ago
Description:	Elephant-sized, though hairier and with longer tusks. The woolly coat helped it survive in ice and snow.

Two famous extinctions
– and how they happened

The Auroch

What was an auroch?

A **wild ox**, much bigger than cattle today.

It roamed across Europe, including Britain, and was very bad tempered! You had to be brave to hunt one.

By the thirteenth century they were only found in central Europe.

What happened to them?

They were probably hunted to extinction. The last auroch died in Poland in 1627.

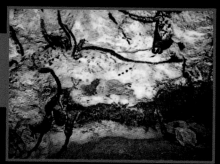

An auroch from a cave painting made thousands of years ago.

The Dodo

What was a Dodo?

A bird, about a metre tall. It lived on the island of Mauritius and couldn't fly.

Before people arrived, there were no predators.

Africa

Mauritius

Were they killed by people?

Some were, but they tasted awful! This was probably not the main reason for their extinction.

People who came to the island brought other animals with them, like dogs, pigs, cats and rats.

Dodos laid their eggs in nests on the ground, and these animals probably ate or destroyed them.

The last Dodo was seen in 1662, though they may have lasted a little longer than that.

Modern extinction timeline

Hunting caused many later extinctions.

This timeline shows some creatures we will never see again.

1870 Atlas Bear

The only bear found in Africa. Hunted to extinction.

1884 Great Auk

A seabird from the North Atlantic. Hunted to death.

1860   1870   1880   1890   1900   1910   1920   193

1883 Quagga

An animal like a zebra from Africa. Hunted to extinction. The last ones died in zoos.

1914 Passenger Pigeon

A very common bird from North America. Hunted to extinction for food.

The passenger pigeon went from 5 billion birds to just nine in less than 100 years.

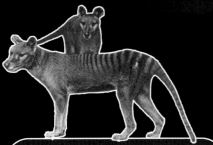

2000 Pyrenean Ibex

Found in Spain. The last animal died in 2000 when a tree fell on her – the first animal to become extinct in the 21st century.

Scientists are trying to clone this animal.

1936 Tasmanian Tiger

Not a tiger at all, though it did have stripes. Extinction caused by loss of habitat and possibly disease.

940   1950   1960   1970   1980   1990   2000   2010

2006 Baiji (Chinese River Dolphin)

Found in the Yangtze river in China. Last seen in 2004, so probably extinct. Wiped out because of habitat loss, fishing and pollution.

1950s Caspian Tiger

Found in the Middle East and Asia. Deliberately wiped out. Some people think they may still exist, but this isn't likely.

Lost – and found

Some animals were thought to be extinct – but then living ones were found! These are called Lazarus species.

Why? There is a person called Lazarus in the bible. He was brought back from the dead.

I'm called the **eyelash gecko**. Can you guess why?

Everybody thought I was extinct, but I was found again in 1994, after a tropical storm.

My biggest threat is from **little fire ants**: they are **alien invaders**: they attack us and sting us.

I'm a **takahe**, a bird that can't fly. I lived in **New Zealand** until 1898. Then the last four of us were killed by humans.

But – surprise! Some more of us were found in 1948. Now there are more than 200 of us left.

I am a **Burchell's zebra**. They thought we were extinct by 1910. But we're not.

I'm a **Lord Howe Island stick insect**. They thought that I was extinct by 1930. Then in 2001 someone found a few of us living under a shrub.

I am 'the rarest insect in the world'.

I'm a **tree frog** from **Costa Rica**. It was thought that we went extinct in the 1980s, but we were spotted again in 2007.

We've been called 'the world's rarest tree frog'.

15

What next?

Could there be another mass extinction?

 Yes!

- The Earth could be hit by a huge comet.

- A giant volcano could erupt, filling the air with dust.

- A nuclear war could wipe out most living things.

Those things aren't very likely to happen, but there is another possible cause.

Climate change could have serious effects on the world's habitats.

- It could become too hot and dry for tropical rainforests to survive.

Melting ice could wipe out many Arctic and Antarctic species.

The **sea** could become **warmer** and **more acid**. Shellfish can't live in water that is very acid.

There is one more species that could be in danger of extinction – **us**!

How could that happen?

There could be a **mass extinction**, or a new, **killer disease**. Or we could lose our **habitat** – the planet Earth – by not looking after it.

We only have one planet.

Of all the animals that have lived on Earth, only one in a thousand are alive now.

Will we still be around in 1,000 years?

The Last Mammoth

Chapter 1:
Hunger

Mukktuk ran his finger over the point of his spear. Sharp – *deadly* – but it had been weeks since he had used it.

He thought about his family, in the village over the hills to the south.

His son Taknen was seven years old. He had been a strong child, but now he was weak. All they had to feed him were roots, and seeds from the grasses. It was not enough.

Taknen needed meat.

Ruglad, the village tracker, appeared in the distance. He waved to the hunters. He had found something!

The hunters ran to meet him.

'Mammoth tracks!' he said. 'In the next valley!'

Mammoth! The herds of mammoth used to come south for the winter, but for three years there had been no sign of them. A mammoth would feed the village right through the winter.

Again, Mukktuk ran his finger over the sharp point of his spear.

Chapter 2:
The storm

The hunters checked the tracks that Ruglad had found. They had expected a herd of mammoths, but there were just two sets of tracks – an adult and a calf.

'The tracks are fresh!' Ruglad said. 'We will catch them with half a day's running!'

'Wait!' Togneth shouted. Togneth was the oldest and wisest of the hunters.

'There is a storm coming. Look at those clouds!'

He was right. But without meat, there was no hope. Grimly, the hunters started to follow the tracks.

An hour later, the snow started to fall. Ruglad was worried. If the snowfall was heavy, the tracks would disappear.

The wind was icy. Mukktuk pulled the bear furs tighter round his body. Heavy snow wouldn't just cover the mammoth tracks. It would cover the tracks of the hunters. Storms could last for days.

The hunters could freeze to death before they found their village again.

Chapter 3:
The attack

The snow fell faster, and the wind blew the freezing flakes into their faces.

'It's no good!' Togneth said. 'We must turn round now!'

But keen-eyed Ruglad has seen something.

'Look! Sheltering behind those rocks!'

The hunters were lucky. The fierce wind would hide their scent from the animal. The wind was so loud it would not hear them coming, either.

Mukktuk was the best hunter with a spear. He was the first to attack.

The spear went in deep. The other hunters were close behind. Maddened with pain, the animal turned on them.

Togneth was not quick enough. The animal's tusk hit him in the chest. He went down with a cry.

At last the animal lay dead. Some of the hunters started to cut it up. Other went to find wood to build a sledge.

The village was saved!

Chapter 4:
The calf

Alone in the growing blizzard, the mammoth calf searched for its mother.

But its mother was piled up in bloody chunks on the hunters' sledge.

The small, exhausted creature pushed on through the snow, and finally reached a frozen river.

The older mammoths would never have let him walk on the ice, but the calf was too young to know the danger ...

'It's a mammoth calf! Really well preserved!' shouted the digger.

The professor rushed over.

'Wonderful! The best I've ever seen!'

'But how did the body survive?'

'It may have fallen through ice into a lake or river. The freezing water would have preserved it.'

'What a brilliant scientist he is!' thought the digger.

'There's nothing that Professor Togneth doesn't know about mammoths!'

Lost Animals word check

alien

carnivore

climate change

endangered

evolution

extinction

fossil

habitat

herbivore

Lazarus species

mammal

mammoth

pollution

predator

preserved

species

volcano